MW00527472

Menopause:
The Anthology

edited by
Cherry Potts
and
Catherine Pestano

ARACHNE PRESS

First published in UK 2023 by Arachne Press Limited
100 Grierson Road, London SE23 1NX
www.arachnepress.com
© Arachne Press 2023
ISBNs
Print 978-1-913665-85-2
eBook 978-1-913665-86-9

Thanks to Muireann Grealy and Liudmyla Lobodzets for their
proofing.

The publication of this book is supported using public funding
by the National Lottery through Arts Council England.

Acknowledgements

A Cabin in the Woods © Lucy Lasasso 2023

A Sudden Ending © Anne Macaulay 2023

A Summer Prematurely Here © Victoria Ekpo 2023

Be Cool © Tina Bethea Ray 2023

Black Armour © Joanne Harris 2023

Breakup © Helen Campbell 2023

China, Flush and *Red Clover and Black Cohosh Days* © Anne Caldwell 2023

Déjà Vu © Sian Northey 2023

Demeter © Elizabeth A Richter 2023

Dried © Susan Cartwright-Smith 2023

Enough Already © Claire Lynn 2023

Evorel © Clare Starling 2023

Fairy Tales for the Over Fifties © Alison Habens 2023

Flashes of Kindness, men-oh-paused – Haibun and *Relieved* © Victoria Bailey 2023

Foreign Land © Ellesar Elhaggagi 2023

From Menarche to Menopause – Top FAQs © Cath Holland 2023

Gutsy Menopausal Woman © Chloe Balcomb 2023

Her Mid-life Performance Review © Ruth Higgins 2023

HUM PBA CK © JP Seabright 2023

Menostop © Kim Whysall-Hammond 2023

Monthly © Tessa Lang 2023

more the use the womb is put to than the womb itself, my vulva & i used to be friends and *Washing Mary* © Jane Ayres 2023

My Wild Fires © Marina Sanchez 2023

Natural Wastage © Anne Eccleshall 2023

Night Sweats © Julie-Ann Rowell 2023

Nuclear Tingle (no one told me how my heart would feel) © Karen F Pierce 2023

Obit: My Last Egg © Susan Bennett 2023

O Womb © Mary Mulholland 2023

On Discovering a New Energy Source © Claire Booker 2023

Over the Bloody Moon © Adele Evershed 2023

Pause © Rachel Playforth 2023

Margaret Mead quotation: Brody, Jane E. "Personal Health." The New York Times, Section C, 17, July 29, 1981.

Menopause:
The Anthology

Contents

Introduction: Catherine Pestano & Cherry Potts

The most powerful force in the world is a menopausal woman with zest.
Margaret Mead, 1950

The subject of menopause is just beginning to break the barrier of taboo, and become a mainstream discussion point, but that discussion has until now been serious, medical, and, we would argue, heterosexual and white. This anthology of poems and short fiction aims to address that, with wild and wonderful writing with humour and anger, relief and distress, by women who have experienced menopause, whether naturally or as a result of surgery; with celebration and grief, and with a healthy dose of views from the global majority and the lesbian, bisexual, non-binary and trans communities.

Though the menopause is traditionally thought of as a life-changing *incident*, the irony is that unless brought on by medical conditions or intervention, no one knows when their last bleed occurred until long after. We therefore think of menopause as a transition: an ellipse rather than an exclamation mark.

For those who are unsure what we are talking about, the menopause transition is a biological state of flux and change usually achieved in mid-life. The perimenopause (not there yet, but on its way) and the post-menopause period (calculated retrospectively as a year after the ending of menstruation) can, between them, last years. These hormonal changes are experienced, to a varying degree, by anyone who was born with female sex organs, women, some non-binary people and trans men; but it can also be part of a broader narrative of mid-life.

Menopause coverage in the media is sharing much useful information about physical, cognitive, emotional and relational issues, which are to some extent being recognised and acted upon in workplaces and doctors' surgeries.

This often unspoken transition affects roughly half the population. With the UK average age of menopause at 51, and life expectancy around 82 years, we have over a third of our lives to live after this transition. 'The change' can offer opportunities to experience new ways of living and renegotiate our relationships with each other and the world. Even the exhaustion that can accompany changes in the body can become a crucible for contemplation, a time to re-evaluate and reflect.

Living through the menopause is often compounded by intersectional oppressions. Misogyny meets racism, homophobia and transphobia. Menopause can be highly medicalised, yet some struggle to have their symptoms recognised, taken seriously or treated. This leads to a lack of autonomy for the menopausal, and a culture of silence and sometimes shame, for those who struggle with symptoms or their treatment. It is important to create meaning from this enormous upheaval in the lives of women.

Poetry and story allow us to express a wide range of responses – sometimes unpalatable, unexpected, joyous, sometimes absurd.

We ran online and face-to-face workshops and asked our contributors to go beyond hot flushes, HRT and empty nest syndrome, and they have. We greeted with joy the humour, anger and outrage that ensued regardless of the individual subject matter. This collection is rich in emotion and bluntness, steeped in metaphor, delving into the surreal. Writing of rare, even unique, phenomena and the difficulties in finding the right help and support, unsympathetic encounters with bosses and doctors are dissected with sharp pens.

Imagination helps us to leap the barriers of how we have been told menopause will affect us, and how we should behave, creating new options for this new phase.

Join us in the new possibilities, even liberations, that lie beyond the time of bleeding.

Cath Holland
From Menarche to Menopause – Top FAQs

How do I arrange delivery?

For the arrival of a girl's menarche, her first blood, she is advised to book early in order to avoid disappointment. If she is allotted a schoolday slot, it means she's chosen an unfortunately busy period. If this does happen, then she must carefully plan the exact time to accept delivery. She should avoid at all costs being in a PE lesson, for example. It could get messy.
Ensure *you* have sufficient menstrual products, paracetamol, and a hot water bottle. Shop for essentials in <u>our online store</u>.

How much will the service cost?

Postage + packing of the service is free, but management and maintenance will cost the average woman approximately £5,000 during her fertile years. Factor in laundry, operating at a slower pace at work or school at badly affected times, and sick days due to cramps, constipation, diarrhoea – or both – feeling bloated, breast tenderness, irritability, tiredness, increased symptoms around an endometriosis diagnosis, mood swings. Our book about this, <u>Choices</u>, is currently at half price.

What are the positives of women having periods? It sounds awful.

Some women feel more connected to a feminine essence, the ebbs and flows of mood – instinctive and somehow primal. Many enthuse at the shared experience of sisterhood. Women who live together in a relationship or as housemates have reported their cycles working in tandem, which is pretty magical, if you think on. Some regard menstruation as a biological advantage, as men do not experience the same sense of being and purpose.

We have gorgeous lunar calendars on which you can have fun and plot ovulation dates together with your friends. Buy two for the price of one <u>here</u>.

My period isn't regular anymore. What are the common causes?

You could be pregnant – congratulations (we hope). No periods for you for a while then! Or you may be suffering from stress or malnutrition or be simply perimenopausal or menopausal. Sign up to our <u>mailing list</u> for all eventualities.

What is the menopause?

The average woman's period becomes intermittent from her mid-forties onwards, then dribbles to a halt. She can no longer get pregnant once fully in menopause although may 'get caught' in peri. That final ovulation and subsequent period can be quite sneaky. Some women say a 'change baby' keeps you young, but make sure to use our impressive range of contraceptives if you don't want to take chances.

Condom and lubricant can be delivered within the hour if needed, <u>order online</u>.

What is the name for a woman's final period?

There isn't one.
Click <u>here</u> for our online shop.

Why is there no name for a woman's final period?

Brexit.
Click here for our online shop.

Are there any downsides to the menopause?

Your body will change as you move into this new, exciting phase of life. Luckily, we can help.

Facial cooling spray £15; try our menstrual face cream – it does not smell, look or feel like it sounds! Perimenopause plumping day cream £25.60, perimenopause revitalizing night cream £27.20, menopause triple action face serum £31.20, menopause night repair £31.45; menstrual shampoo, conditioner, serum £22 each. Take no notice of negative reviews of our hair serum planted by our competitors. Stay clear of the scalp foam stuff by inferior brands, it makes your hair well crispy. Ours makes your locks silky soft, and fuller.
Order online.

Are there any holistic remedies to manage menopause symptoms?

If you have gym membership, try weight-bearing exercise classes to strengthen bones and offset osteoporosis. Dark chocolate increases oestrogen, nom-nom. Chocolate is calorific and weight gain is a problem for some average women, but a wraparound dress works wonders, shrinks the waist. Our special night-time wear combats night sweats, made as it is from cotton/ linen/ bamboo/ silk/ wool/ cashmere/ hemp, pulling moisture away from the body allowing it to naturally evaporate.
We've got clothes in stock in colours and patterns to compliment

the pink-cheeked, starting at £35.99. Join our <u>online menopause group</u> with optional breakout rooms, £100pa.

What if I want my fertility back?

Once the average woman's body clock has ticked its last tock, that's it. The workings thin and wear out. On the upside, did you know women in their forties and fifties are sexually most compatible with men in their twenties?
Our dating app launches soon.

Can you return, swap or repair my fertility?

Not after the guarantee expires. The service returns to the manufacturer once the environment you provide exceeds its Best Before date. When a menstrual cycle stops pedaling, it won't move again. The Chinese call the menopause the second spring; we suggest you embrace your new-found freedom.
In return, you get a life with lots of opportunities, which you can purchase from us.

What about my statutory rights?

Read the small print, translated into Braille, and different languages including average middle-aged-woman-speak.
Avoid FOMO – orders are <u>50% off for a limited time</u>.

Is there a similar product on the market?

Your service is discontinued. It was on loan. Temporary. With our products, the average woman copes very well.
We have a very wide range of vitamins, and menopausal pick-me-ups.

How can I find out if I'm an average woman?

Click here for our online shop.

Is the lack of substitutes related to Brexit?

Red tape is not the issue.
All you need is available in our online store.

I am not happy with your customer service.

We are working towards a dedicated menopause helpline.
Further FAQs can be found in our online resources.

Who do I complain to?

We are working towards a dedicated menopause helpline.
Click here for our online shop, next day delivery is available.

I don't feel seen or listened to.

Wear purple.
We have lots of purple stuff on sale. Explore our store. Please.

Why on earth didn't I value my fertility when I had it?

I wouldn't be stuck here doing this job if I had the answer to that.
Now, can I take your order?

Rachel Playforth
Pause

But wait, I am still centre stage
living at full tilt
in glorious technicolour –
the greatest show!
I am aerialist and ringmaster,
strongman and clown,
bareback rider, bearded lady.
The big top still billows
in orange and pink,
my lives are not ready to fold,
but the guy ropes have loosened
and something is flapping
or tearing…
wait –

Anne Macaulay
A Sudden Ending

Bumping into my old doctor in the shops
I blurted out about the cancer
the proposed hysterectomy

He said in his usual kind but direct way
Get rid of it you don't need it now
I knew he still cared I felt reassured

Weeks later there I was walking out slowly
from Fuschia ward to the car thinking on
the advice don't even lift a kettle

I didn't miss buying tampons
or the flow of blood between my legs
or cramping cramping pain

And I was told how I missed the sweats
the mood swings the unkind build up
to the end of fertility

But I didn't feel less like a woman
just like a woman who for a while
lumbered along in slow motion

Of course enforced menopause wasn't all
smooth – HRT patches sometimes slid off
in the shower or in summer heat

And then a storm that made PMT
seem like nothing at all
would take possession

until a new circle of plastic adhered
set my chemistry in equilibrium
gave a lift to my womanly stride.

Marina Sánchez
My Wildfires

Torching me in public
in private, day and night
I offer myself

to their incandescence
as they rise from my sacrum,
blaze through my core

licking my body, stripping
me bare. I'm the crimson
witness as the fuel of years

feeds the flames: memories
glow, regrets rage, shame
is consumed, grief devoured.

All the sorrows that steal
my breath as my shoulders
round to shelter my heart

I sacrifice them all.
I am fire, offering, desire.

Genevieve Carver
The Grandmother Hypothesis

Apart from humans the only animals who experience the menopause are toothed whales including narwhals orcas and belugas scientists think it's because in these groups females are valued beyond their reproductive capabilities the older ones take on important social roles like grandmothers and haven't you had grandmothers or women who were like grandmothers slinging fish right into your gullet just when you were about to sink and haven't you wondered why after the bleeding stopped you grew flippers a thick layer of blubber and a nine-foot tusk spiralling from your upper lip and did you read the poem coiled inside the helix apart from humans the only animals who write poems are scarlet macaws and jellyfish scientists don't understand their poems but a junior laboratory technician was once moved to tears and years later when she threw herself off Sydney Harbour Bridge they found a jellyfish verse in her pocket they did an experiment in which narwhal grandmothers were asked to write poems but all they did was smash down the walls of the tank with their knitting needles they had folk songs trembling in their blowholes.

Tina Bethea Ray
Be Cool

Eavesdropping on the aunties was child's play when I was younger. I was limber and light on my feet, so I could easily sneak in and hide under the table or behind a couch. I remember them talking about hot flashes and menopause but had no clue what they meant.

Frankly, I thought they were complainers.

The chatter was always the same, eliciting one of two typical responses: laughter or shaking their heads.

There was talk of sheets soaked from sweat, cravings for chocolate, or non-interest in sex.

It absolutely made no sense to me. But it sounded juicy.

I just wanted my aunties to lose themselves in laughter.

How do you wake up covered in sweat? And what was sex?

By my late forties, I began to wake up in night sweats.

I'd be sitting in a meeting at work and need to excuse myself to go to the bathroom to splash cold water over my face, but not only that, I also needed to take a paper towel with me back to the meeting.

One of my creative cousins made me a hand-held leather fan and shipped it from three states away for me to keep in my purse.

I learned to dress in sundresses and sandals.

Now, I'm the auntie. My nieces can climb under the table and listen to me, as auntie talks about night sweats, cravings, non-interest in sex. One day when they're going through the change, maybe they too will recollect those conversations.

It's one cycle that will continue.

And maybe they'll discover, as I have, that there's only one or two appropriate places to go after a hot flash brought on from a hot shower, even in winter – the garage or outdoors.

Jane Ayres
more the use the womb is put to than the womb itself

i don't normally write this kind of poem / but i'm so angry at a remark made on a tv show about a fictional female character who is an older woman / in which the presenter commented that this female fictional character hadn't experienced life / because she never married or gave birth to children / but nevertheless possessed a sharp incisive mind (the character that is) / & although i'm sure the person who said this never intended to cause offence / nevertheless / i found this deeply offensive / because it implied (more than implied) / that women who never marry or don't / can't / have kids are somehow less than / that their experiences have no value / & i thought about my late godmother / who never ticked those boxes & devoted her life to helping her local community & generations of children / did her life have less meaning? / her experiences less validity? / but her late mum / (my late grandmother) / had 15 children / so was her existence worth 15 times more than my godmother's? / or mine? (my womb was surgically removed) / & back to the programme / which did not describe a particular male fictional character in a similar vein / despite said character never marrying or procreating / his achievements & mental acuity & intelligence being the only aspects celebrated / because society tends not to level this kind of judgement on men / & / imo / regardless of gender / if we measure the worth of a life (& why do we even need to measure this?) / perhaps it should be in relation to a person's positive contribution to the lives of others / but (as I said earlier) / why this unhealthy obsession with measuring / assessing / comparing / evaluating / judging / assuming / grading / ranking everything / & why can't people just   be

Victoria Bailey
Flashes of Kindness

I wrestled with burning in line
until she waved me over
told me to sit down
behind her counter
turned her fan on me
and smiled.

Erica Borgstrom
Women of your age

She said that phrase
Over the phone
After checking my date of birth

What?
Just turned 35
Less than two weeks ago
What does women of my age even mean?

My friends are having babies.
Aren't I in my prime?
Bleeding, brain fog, bloating, nauseating pain.
The work, romantic dates with partners, and clothes
left ruined in the wake.

It's normal
For women of your age
Is it? None of my friends talk about it.
Try the pill. Or the coil.
You're done with kids, right?

Another doctor suspects cancer.
But doesn't say it. Just worrying symptoms
For a woman of your age.
Urgent referral after urgent referral.
Long waits.
Results – we don't know. Maybe stress.

Women of our age.
Left to wait. Count the days.
It could be ten years yet.

Julie-Ann Rowell
Night Sweats

are the first indication; she gives into them, sliding out
of damp sheets and brewing green tea in a favourite cup,

shaky like a young tree, but no longer supple.
Then comes a time when she no longer recognises herself.

The GP says it's common for the middle-aged.
She didn't think of herself as middle-aged,

but he could talk, in his trimmed grey everything. I'll never
wear grey again, she decides, disposing of his pills.

Heat visits, like putting her head in the oven, or standing in a desert.
She's never visited a desert, sand and sand-mites, hot wind.

Flush doesn't cover it. It takes more than months, this drying up.
No more blood, but in her head, rising.

She goes out one day to gather washing off the line, and lets the rain
wet her through, wondering if she is being watched.

It's as if everyone sees her as mad, in that circular way.
The drinking of wine, tears, the poring over old photographs

of mother, grandmother. The shrivelling vagina.
The thinking about death all the time.

The child she did not allow herself to have.
How her thighs ache when she climbs the stairs.

Tired out, a spent light bulb, pearl and dim. Shops no longer a draw.
The need for seeds, honey, figs and dates, coffee she hates.

Emotional explosions she can't account for. Mind hiccupping.
Remembering her mother going through the same, and not
understanding.

She'd never heard of menopause and mother didn't explain.
She just slowly disappeared with all her regrets unspoken.

Anne Caldwell
Red Clover and Black Cohosh Days

These are days of solitude, quiet pleasure. Free from all the prittle-prattle of love. I'm a misplaced whistle in a kitchen drawer, a bottle of damson gin lounging in the dresser or a long-distance runner, backpack crammed with Kendal Mint Cake and electrolyte-water. I'm nobody's plaything. My mornings are envelope-sharp and free from all distraction. The Tiger of Love does not crouch at the end of my rowing boat, striped pelt of desire taut over bone and muscle, with that slow, particular yawn before a pounce.

Lucy Lasasso
A Cabin in the Woods

Once there was a woman, Bria, who lived alone in a cabin in the woods. She was not a young woman, but neither was she old. She had seen the leaves fall and the birds fly away and return in spring many times. In the autumn she picked berries. Some years her basket was full, but in other years she searched for hours, looking under the leaves of every bush and walking all day through the forest to gather a mere handful. She didn't worry. She plucked a leaf from a rare plant deep in the woods and chewed it to sate her hunger.

The cabin was as cosy as a bird's nest. There were bright rugs on the floor and thick, soft blankets on the bed and covering her old armchair. In winter a fire blazed in the grate, dying down to glowing embers through the night.

Bria cooked soups and stews flavoured with the wild herbs she picked and dried. The smell of thyme and sorrel filled the room. She was alone, but she was not lonely. She liked to listen to the foxes prowling at night and the badgers lumbering through the undergrowth. When the river was in full spate, she could hear the rush of water. Sometimes, borne on the east wind, she caught the sound of Hefaesta, the blacksmith, at work at her anvil. When the wind dropped Bria would wake to the chiming of the church clock far away in the valley, as the sky turned pink, and the birds began to sing. They were happy times.

But little by little things changed.

She tossed and turned all night. The chimes of the church clock were loud and jarring to her ears, striking every quarter all through the night. In the mornings she was exhausted, and lay in her rumpled bed until the sun streamed in, showing every speck of dust and every streak on the windowpanes.

Bria was as hot as a furnace in hell. Her soul was as dark as a moonless night. Her food was as tasteless as gruel without salt. Her limbs ached and her hair was dry as straw. She picked up the hand mirror that had been her mother's. It was finely made, and the only thing she owned of any value to the world outside her cabin and wood. She looked at her gaunt reflection: dark shadows circled her eyes, skin once smooth and clear, now wrinkled and dull. She knew then that she had been cursed.

Restless, she trod the paths of the forest back and forth until her aching body demanded sleep.

The blacksmith paused in her work to watch her go by. Bria's eyes were cast down, and she did not greet Hefaesta as she usually would.

She will not know me, Bria thought, for I am so changed.

Frowning, Hefaesta turned back to her work.

As another pink dawn streaked the sky and the clock struck five times, Bria wrapped bread, apples and dried berries in a bundle and set off to see the witch woman who lived across the river. She wound a soft cloth around her mother's mirror and hid it under her provisions.

She walked out in the cool of the morning with her basket and a stick she had cut from a hazel tree.

Bria trudged by the side of the rushing river until she found a crossing place. The shock of the icy water nearly made her turn back, but she pushed herself on, using her stick to stay upright and cross the river. The water foamed around her up to her waist, and her dress floated out behind her.

At last she reached the other side and lay for a while on the grass until the morning sun dried her. She was so quiet that a young deer came close to graze, now and then lifting its head to look at her with wide eyes.

The cave of the witch woman was nearby, an opening in the rocks hidden behind a grove of silver birch trees. Their bark gleamed white against the hard, black rocks, and their leaves fluttered and shivered in the breeze.

The witch crouched in the sun at the mouth of the cave, waiting for her. A strange striped creature sat at her feet, playing with the corpse of a tiny bird, tossing it up in the air and pouncing on it. It was neither cat nor dog. It had the yellow eyes and pointed ears of a cat and the powerful body of a dog, with a long, lashing tail.

The witch stood up. Her feet were bare and filthy, and she was tall, with dark hair piled up on her head so she looked even taller. She wore a red dress that trailed on the dusty ground. It must have been a fine dress once, but now it was stained, ripped and torn, with dark patches under the arms.

'I know why you have come,' she said.

Her voice was harsh, and when she spoke, she showed two pointed gold teeth like gleaming fangs. The creature who played at her feet glared at Bria and hissed. The witch spoke gently, and the animal retreated to the back of the cave, so that all Bria could see were its two yellow eyes, glowing from the shadows.

'If you give me the mirror,' said the witch, 'I will make you well.'

Bria hesitated. The mirror was the most precious thing she possessed. Just to hold it and touch it brought back the memory of her mother, and her mother's love for her. But her body was weary, and her spirit was tired.

Before she could speak, the witch reached into the basket and grabbed the mirror. She pulled off the cloth and held it up to her face, laughing. Her reflection in the glass was young and beautiful with shining eyes and smooth skin.

'I will make you like this again,' she said.

Bria couldn't move. She felt as if her arms had been pinned to her sides. But then she pictured her mother's face and heard the sound of her singing as she worked.

She lunged at the witch, snatched the mirror back and ran from the cave.

'You fool,' screamed the witch.

The striped creature bounded out from the cave after Bria. She felt a sharp pain as it sank claws like hooked daggers into her leg and clung on. She could not shake it off. She staggered to the riverbank and tumbled into the water still clutching the mirror.

She felt the creature let go. Hissing and bedraggled, it stood on the bank, back arched, glaring with spiteful yellow eyes. Bria was carried off by the current and swept furiously down the river, battered against rocks and struggling for breath. Cold to the bone, at last she managed to grab a willow branch. With a strength she did not know she possessed, she pulled herself onto a stony inlet, the mirror cracked, but gleaming, still in her hand.

The blacksmith found her there as the light was fading from the sky and the birds fell silent with the coming of night. Bria's body was small and light in Hefaesta's arms as she carried her back to her cottage and tended to her cuts and bruises. Bria's leg was slashed with angry red welts where the witch's creature had clawed her. The blacksmith cleaned her cuts with salt water and covered them with a poultice of moss and herbs. For three days and three nights Bria slept in the blacksmith's narrow bed. Hefaesta slept near her on rush matting, waking now and then as Bria called out for her mother.

When at last the fever went, Bria woke. The blacksmith was by her bedside, smiling, holding up the cracked silver mirror. Not until then had Bria paid any heed to Hefaesta's soft brown eyes and her gentle voice.

'You were holding this tight in your hand and wouldn't let it go,' Hefaesta said, 'not until I laid you down.'

Bria felt life rise again in her. She looked into the mirror and saw then that she was how she was, and that she was happy.

Jane Ayres
Washing Mary

We were bathing Vi,
one of the elderly female residents,
when the other care assistant
said gently *Time to wash Mary.*
Make her nice and clean.

Vi, laughing at the familiar instruction,
rubbed flannel and soap vigorously
between her thighs beneath the bubbles.
My first day in the job, I was seventeen,
uncomfortable witnessing
such an intimate act.

I never knew where the phrase came from
or who Mary was.

Now, so many years later,
I'm soaking in the bath,
touching my inner and outer labia,
noticing their looseness, lips no longer
tight and neat as they once were
although my clitoris still responds
(mostly) if given appropriate encouragement
(good old clit!)

Now, I try without success to visualise
my altered internal landscape
– everything gone –
except a re-sculpted
vaginal sleeve (which always makes me think of
a hand-knitted cardigan, pastel blue).

According to the surgeon, the hysterectomy created
a space the size of a fist. A small space. Even so,
it's hard not to attempt to fill a space. (Apparently
your bowels drop into the newly created cavity).

Folding myself into
warm soothing water
I lean back,
tenderly cup my vulva in my palm
and say hello to Mary.

Sian Northey
Déjà vu

It passed
without incident.
Nada, zilch, sweet FA.
I tell a lie
– I did at times feel really, really cold.
My thermostatic malfunction
perversely the opposite
of all the other girls.
So I didn't mention that.
And once again I was
killing time
between the gym and the chain-link fence,
wearing the wrong shoes
and not in love with David Cassidy.

Alyson Hallett
Shape-shift

The body goes on doing what the body does best.
Bleeding. Digesting. Dreaming. Some nights

it takes the old ovaries to the forge and
heats them to the point of combustion. Every

phoenix is ash first. The body doesn't ask why.
It makes whatever needs to be made.

In Spanish the word carne means meat and flesh.
I don't know why that's important, but it is. Not

the faraway places, not the beaches or palaces but
the country of the body, these continents of brain

and womb. The way meat with your name
can sweat and change. In Key West I learned

that a grub liquefies before becoming a butterfly.
The word menopause is not ugly. It's shamanic.

Susan Bennett
Obit: My Last Egg

Inspired by Victoria Chang

My last egg died without making any fuss
sometime in the early years of the 21st century.
There was no service, no headstone, no urn,
not even a plastic carton as some eggs enjoy.
No one sent flowers or made a donation to a
worthy cause. No casseroles or finger sandwiches
were delivered by church ladies. My last egg
was the sole remaining survivor of an extended family
of four hundred thousand, her siblings having been
subjected to a forced migration that began in 1967,
the summer of love, and continued with gruesome
regularity until my last egg died
alone and forgotten,
even by me.

Cheryl Powell
Woman's Work

It's off again. Prowling. Snarling out warnings. A bestial thing. What can I do? Wombs break loose from their moorings sometimes, go hunting, seek vengeance. Every menopausal woman knows that.

I take painkillers. Try to decompress.

This meeting is a career-changer; I need to be calm. But my unruly womb is shitting last-gasp hormones into my brain, stirrings of violence, anxiety. There it goes, elbowing over my bladder, kicking past my spleen, leaning in, sluggish and heavy, shedding its ever-diminishing lining into my pelvic cavity.

So, here we are. Two of them seated side-by-side behind the desk. I smile at Dirk, Head of Talent, half-expecting a song, or a soft-shoe shuffle as he announces my promotion. No. Face blank as sticking plaster. Then, line manager, Baz, talent-less, looking down, checking his crotch. Unexceptional, dead-eyed detachments from upper management. My uterine artery flexes.

A flurry of action: stiff smiles, flaccid handshakes, and I'm asked to take a seat.

Dirk slides an unexpected letter towards me; misdemeanours – time-keeping, absenteeism, insubordination. Baz inspects his tie. An incompetent liar.

'Aaah!' My womb squeezes through my colon; a fat mouse lugging its fibroidal bulk towards my stomach, dying ovaries clutched in spiny fingers.

'Oh!' Stabs of pain, like raw darkness, panic.

'Are you unwell?' Dirk flicks a hopeful glance towards a box

39

of tissues on the desk.

'No. It's just, you know, a bit of men...' I stumble.

'Men...?'

'Meno ... ahh! … womb trouble.'

Their rinsed out faces are suddenly crimped with terror.

My womb has views of its own. 'You heard, dickheads,' it says. 'Womb!'

'It's rather ...over-active.' I grind my teeth.

Men like Dirk and Baz fear wombs, especially over-active ones. Wombs have lethal potential; they might get organised.

Right now, my womb is climbing my windpipe. Sliding over my tongue; metallic taste. 'We can take the bastards out,' it whispers. My mouth fizzes and smokes as I heave it up. Dirk and Baz recoil, facial muscles twitching. I launch it across the desk, hot and smouldering, a bloody rosette that lands on Dirk's lapel, and he screams, his little beige face contorted with horror as it leaps across to Baz's chin, clinging on, and he mouthing the air like a suffocating carp.

I slide the letter back.

Silence.

The two look at each other and sniff the air, eyes wide, as if detecting mustard gas. But it's worse than they can imagine; the scent of menstrual blood and bat-shit hormones. It will never leave them. Years of PTSD.

I rise, then. And wait. My womb is shuddering down the front of Baz's suit, a slimy trail as it inches its way back to me, slides into place. Dirk withdraws the letter, cannot look at Baz. They will never speak of this again.

Outside, past the main office, the head of engineering is flushed pink, dabbing sweat from her neck, in dangerous mood. Elsewhere in the building, another hysterical womb detonates, but all I hear are men's voices.

The poor darlings are screaming. They've been hit.

Victoria Bailey
Relieved

I cried
when my periods started.
I sighed
when they returned after birth.
But, oh,
was I so happy
when they stopped.

Jessica Manack
The Other Side of Nowhere

When the door closes for the last time, do they
know it's the last time, my little almosts?
Do they know there will be no more chances
to jostle and queue, hope for a place at the precipice?

Why do we call it meno*pause?*
Pause implies a break, a commercial,
we'll be right back after these messages,
nothing final, no mention of cessation.

So: they wait in their infinite line,
prepared, with the monthly opened door, to leap,
already waiting decades for their chance,
accompanying my rudiments in my mother's womb.

Is it so hard to close the door on possibility
that we can't even say the word? Like when I leave
the knife beside the sink in case I need to dress
another slice of bread, or make a midnight cup of tea.

Or is it because sometimes it happens,
sometimes an octogenarian feels a twinge
and knows these flutters aren't phantoms,
knows a spark has once again caught,

she once again embodies magic?
Who will tell them to keep or not keep
their vigil, poised and ready, hoping hopelessly,
whether or not the odds are in their favour?

Anne Caldwell
Flush

I'm molten rock spilling out from the earth's crust, a lava flow of destruction swallowing all that stands before me. I don't sleep for weeks. I stare through the window into the early hours before dawn breaks, crocosmia lucifer lighting up the garden. I've been simmering for years until my skin's so hot to the touch, no one will come near me. My grandmother was in service, with a flat iron in the fire and a mountain of sheets. My mother hoarded anger, shut it up with cut glass, wedding silver, blinking away in a darkened pantry. Never blowing her top.

Ellesar Elhaggagi
Foreign Land

I'm a man. I am.
In a body that feels like a foreign land.
A body that has given me children
a body that I've got used to managing,
to having to hide.

Now I'm thrown something new,
particularly female.
Menopause? Really?
I can't handle any more.

I am already negated:
wrong pronouns, wrong titles,
glares and stares… But my body…
As if panic attacks, anxiety and depression
weren't enough.

HRT: is it something for me?
More hormone chaos to endure?
It's testosterone my body craves.
Perhaps I could join a social support group?
Women's day or a female meet-up?

Perhaps, if being a woman
was something I could still pretend to be.
I cannot give back
My identity.

Alison Habens
Fairy Tales for the Over Fifties

This starts on your eighteenth birthday –
fifty is nothing unless you recall being young and lovely.
The moment you crossed the bridge, bit the apple, let down your hair,
sowed the magic beans (if you know what I mean)
and mopped up the spilt fairy dust in that transformation scene,

the ride home at twelve in a hollowed-out squash
kissing some frog, sheathed in princess-pink satin,
that night you climbed the bean stalk,
nibbled the gingerbread knocker
and gave the Pied Piper his rat infestation.

Fee Fi Fo Fum; it begins when you sang the other f-word,
ripped into two legs like a little mermaid:
who knew girls could huff, puff and blow the house down?
That night you pulled the enormous turnip

things really were once-upon-a-time, then
cross between spell and shopping list,
enchantment and bank statement,
your life was three wishes, spent in a cave of jewels,
though, on reflection, it could have been a dank basement
and a bottle of Guinness.

Thirty looks like happily-ever-after until you get there,
a cavern of glittering gemstones or
Lego littering the hall carpet in the hung-over dawn.
Too late to rub the lamp, lady, the genie's out,
you're at the sharp end of fairy tales now.

Wearing the red shoes, you never stop dancing,
in the glass slippers, you tip-toe on shards,
with ruby shoes on you glimpse the green faces
and pointed ears of old friends and colleagues.
Racing the retail arcade of your fourth decade,
to-do list longer than your bridal veil

because, congratulations: you got the golden egg
the buried treasure, the grail, the gift of eternal life…
the goal of all romance already; the baby or babies
and now, with a squirt of that starry spermatozoa
from your fairy godmother's tool, you have so been to the ball.

The snow white laundry of school shirts
endless red apple of lunchboxes
seven dwarves of the kindergarten drop-off,
having been up since the sun rose over Narnia/
Nirvana/Neverland/wherever – you've nit-combed Goldilocks,
clipped Daddy Bear's toenails, worn Baby Bear's Ready Brek.
You are still a princess, but their wish is now your command.

Magic wand in right hand, pen, sword, cigarette in the left
briefcase over one shoulder, baby bag over the other,
broomstick between the legs, carrier bag of groceries
balanced on your foot, precious child's eggbox art
under your armpit, pet lead looped around your wrist.
Racing the packed amusement park of your character arc
'My, what big boobs you have': all the better to survive fairyland –
the PhD's not your highest qualification; it's 34D –

but you're gradually changing from Riding Hood to Wolf
because, now appearing only in crowd scenes,
you are lonely, and though you carry
a basket of homemade goodies wherever you go,
you're hungry.

So you eat the three little pigs
you eat the three Billy Goats Gruff
you eat the ugly duckling
Poison apple, poison banana, poison Charon fruit
you bought one and you got one free
you've spooned from the bottomless porridge pot: now what?

By fifty you're on the sliding scale from Wolf to Granny
yet still supposed to feel a pea through a pile of mattresses
you've let down your hair, let down your skin, let down your teeth
it's no longer 'your carriage awaits' but how 'you carries yer weight',
and anyway, you ate the pumpkin.

The godmother turns out to be your real (dead) mother
and twice or thrice upon a time you learn that trolls can really hurt.
Potion dependency may become an issue…
also, passion deficiency, when you've told Tom Thumb
a thousand times it's not size that counts, and anyway, after
a certain age, all men are Wee Willie Winkie.

The best bit is how many pets you can get into
a story for the over fifties;
so many talking animals offering motivational chats,
though your Puss in Boots is balding, with wrinkly leather –
snap fingers, sparks fly – Sleeping Beauty; woken up from a long nap
aware that you're a hundred and sixteen years old,
and about to make mincemeat out of the handsome prince.

That's the last time you wish upon a star.
It's so annoying: when you spin straw into golden hair
and everyone likes it better the way it was before.
It's so upsetting: when you don your old magical colour-changing
gown and they don't let you into the ball.
It's so embarrassing: when you look in the mirror-mirror-on-the-wall
and it whispers 'the wicked witch is you, bitch';

unclear as a glass slipper that's been in the dishwasher,
as the genie's lamp you haven't dared rub for a decade,
you can still hear the tinkly laughter of that reflective bastard
as you ask:
When are we all going to start living happily-ever-after?

Joanne Harris
black armour

transforming my tight little girl curls into the wavy wet tresses of a 1980s-style Jheri Curl to mirror my mom's tresses. only to finally transform into straight dry brittle dead-ends attempting to mirror white women tresses.

transforming my tight little unshed uterus into the beginning of a lifetime departure of black royal beauty. only to finally transform into a bloody useless knot of tumours filled with pain and failing to live her destiny of womanhood.

tackling my coarse brittle hair between my hands as i add white cream to my royal black hair to mirror white women tresses. only to take away from my ancestral heritage of beautiful black tresses.

tackling my painful uterus as it sheds and fills my pads, tampons and panties with dark blood. only to stain and ruin my favourite dresses and steal my heritage as a black queen.

tracing my oily straight flat-ironed hair as she moves against my body and loves me as if i'm whole and full of unique untouched beauty. only to share that i'm not complete as she watches me add the white cream.

tracing my belly as my uterus fills with our growing baby boy as i feel him grow and move like a black king trying to take his throne. only to furrow my brow in worry as i feel him refusing to turn.

tugging and pulling my coarse hair into fraudulent synthetic braids with singed ends thumbed into knots to keep my baby boy safe from the white cream. only to scratch the rash upon my shoulders and back as little black bumps form for my little black king.

tugging my full belly side to side, up and down to the emergence of our king, finally entering his world. only to still feel the pressure of motherhood upon my body with no relief, only shaking, seizing and riddled in pain.

taking my beautiful king upon my breast to feed and bond like only a mother and son are able. only to be bowed in pain from the continuous painful knots upon my belly.

taking my hair from its false braids to again add the white cream as i prepare to return to the white woman's work. only to return to more dominance and less pay.

teaching my son to talk and watching his strong legs walk the floors of our home. only to send him to a white woman's care. she teaches him to read.

teaching my hair to curl from the flat-iron as grease seeps into my scalp each morning before entering the white woman's work. only to feel baldness begin to emerge throughout my hair.

talented hands are swift upon the keyboard and i regain my strength and voice and my blackness emerges from darkness. only to be seen as a threat to the white woman at her desk.

talented hands throughout my scalp preparing for white cream, when i hear the sista say, "you're going to lose your hair." only i can't understand her words because they are jumbled in my head.

tears begin to fall as my black pride grows as my small coarse hair emerges from under the sista's hands and i watch the white woman's hair fall upon the floor. only as my worry grows with each step when i return to the white woman's work.

tears begin to fall as my black body begins to ache and bleed without stopping; ruining more panties and dresses. only to have my fears confirmed when the surgeon looks into my eyes and i hear her say, "you're going to lose your uterus," without sadness, simply fate.

timid hands roam my small afro as i gaze at my reflection and i build upon the strength of my ancestors as i prepare to enter the white woman's battle ground. only to be riddled with the feeling of dread realising that i can't escape the clutches of whiteness.

timid fingertips roam my broken body as my lover listens to my pleas to the doctor, begging her not to take my ovaries too. only to be told that she will do her best and feeling the all too familiar dread of disadvantage.

toughness emergences from my body as i lift my strong black afro that is now tinged with grey from the bed after surgery and ask the question. only to be told that my uterus and ovaries are both gone; intertwined in a bloody useless knot of tumours.

toughness disappears as i am consumed with sadness and despair. only to be reminded that this was my own doing by falling prey to adding white cream to my royal black hair to mirror white women tresses.

tantalizing hands roam my thick coarse hair from my lover's touch, stretching and begging for passion. only to be pulled tighter, harder with no pain, only freedom and joy.

tantalizing happiness arises from my body from the absence of pain and the joy of beautiful movement as i run and play with my king. only to be completely free from the white woman's cream.

Helen Campbell
Breakup

The moon has given me up.
She has left me alone in this still space.
Each day the same. An equal pace.
I no longer wax and wane with her.
The months blur into each other.

The moon has abandoned me
But she left desire behind. As useful
As a fork without a handle! Who will
Look at me now? The eyes
Of the young slip away from me.

The moon has discarded me.
Just like a man you could say.
Edging away slowly, slowly
Until they're altogether gone.
Unnoticed. Unlamented.

The moon has walked away from me.
No going back. Nothing to be done.
I will turn my face. I will follow the sun.
There are paths ahead entangled,
But only one certain ending.

Jane Ayres
my vulva & I used to be friends

but these days we barely speak
hardly acknowledge each other's existence
& I miss our chats
me squatting on the bathroom floor
you reflected back
in the mirror propped between my
thighs   open wide
checking all areas remain
operational
in full working order
ready for action.
Now I can't bring myself to look.

Once
guests were regularly invited to
enter the vestibule
come inside & stay awhile
You've changed. Of course you have.
So have I.

I used to enjoy prodding &
poking but since oestrogen
(obliterated)
left the building
skin thins & tears
lips rip & snag.
Paper cuts &
I am violet.

Kim Whysall-Hammond
Menostop

There is drought
the cave of my uterus has run dry
no longer will days haze
with pain
no longer will cramps stamp
me down

I am filled with vast potentialities
as green joy bursts open
like buds in Spring

Kavita A Jindal
Shamans In Luburbia

'I was told that if you smear the blood from your first period on your face you will never experience problems of severe pain or irregularity.' Pia made a face. 'Well, blow me down. What happened thirty-seven years later, huh? How many years have I suffered lately?'

'Did you do that? Smear the blood?' I'm trying not to sound too incredulous.

'Yes, not only that, the elder ladies in our village told me to put an onion under my left armpit and hop for five minutes every time on the first day of my menses and I wouldn't smell.' She sighs. 'I did that too, just for three months though.'

I giggle at the thought of immaculate Pia with an onion in her armpit. I'm curious to know more. 'Was this advice widespread in the Philippines or just in your village?'

'Don't know,' she says with a dainty shrug. 'If we'd had daughters instead of sons we wouldn't be imparting old wives' tales, would we?'

I consider. 'There were some traditions I might have passed on, even if I'm not sure about their efficacy. Rub a pure silver bowl on a girl baby's body. For smooth hairless skin. My mother said she did it for me.'

'But you weren't told anything about your first blood, were you?'

'No,' I admit. I realise I don't know a single tradition about periods in India. Except that menstruating females, of any age, were not allowed inside the temples. The gods might be swayed by polluting blood and the impurity of womanhood;

presumably they don't already know everything, they might be dishonoured, or distracted, as one priest put it. From what? From the fact of life itself? Distracted from being a god? The goddesses are apparently alarmed by menstruation too, because even in the temples dedicated to a powerful goddess, a menstruating woman is forbidden to enter. The idol loses her power if a 'live' power comes within her orbit. I mull over these traditions, thinking that, in truth, it might have made sense for women to stay home, as they did in every part of the world, until it became easier to remain active while on your period; our gods and goddesses need to evolve with us – can someone tell the priests?

Pia is waiting for something from me. 'Nope,' I say. 'Can't think of anything to do with first menses. But maybe applying that blood on your face is your secret – you do have wonderful glowing skin.' I sound like an advertisement, but I mean it. At fifty-five her skin looks plump and soft.

She touches her face. 'That's just genes. Like you are longlimbed and your arms and legs haven't thickened.'

Pia doesn't say the rest of me has, she doesn't need to.

We glance at the pushchairs and four mums at the bigger table next to us. Our weekly brunch in this café, popular with new mothers, is her idea. Pia likes looking at the babies and remarking to me loudly 'thank god that's over'. She likes scrutinising her manicured nails and sometimes tossing her freshly shampooed hair. 'I was always a mess, never could get my act together to have my nails or hair looking good.'

I can't imagine her dishevelled, but I nod. 'Me too,' I say. In my case, it wasn't just varnishing my nails that I never got round to, I couldn't be bothered dressing in anything that wasn't comfortable. It helped that my workplace dressing was casual too and I didn't often have to go into an office. That habit of comfortable clothes has persisted. I was always sleep deprived when my children were young. Since then sound sleep is the most beautiful sensation of all, even when I have an abundance of it.

We seem to have set something off at the next table because we're hearing stories of first periods from many different places. This is why I love eavesdropping and why I love London and also Luburbia. That's my name for our part of Greater London. We're in suburbia and in London, both. In Luburbia we are boastful about the fact we have a pond and a buzzing café life. Today, rows of cherry trees cheer up the grey sky. They thrust their blooms up, in their pink brightness and white delicacy, reaching up, above us, challenging the gloom the sky sends down.

The neighbouring table is in full flow about first periods, traditions and tales. The café owner, Alban, keeps his head down, but like us, he's listening. I learn from an ebullient talker among the mums that in South India in some communities a girl's coming of age is marked by celebration, she's given gifts and a half-sari. A half grown-up way of dressing. This is after she's isolated for a while, and this also means her period is 'announced'.

'The most embarrassing week of my life,' says the woman telling the story.

'At least you didn't get slapped,' someone pipes up.

'What?' the others shriek.

'We get slapped. My grandma slapped me. Only for the first period. It's the done thing.'

I can't tell where this tradition is from. I missed what the person said. Greece?

'I'd like to know what menopause traditions there are,' I growl at Pia.

Now she giggles like the sweet girl she must've been. 'Oh, as if you care. All we two do is moan about how terrible it is.'

'Well, it has been for us,' I point out. Pia and I became properly acquainted in the waiting room of a hormone specialist. One morning I arrived for my first consultation, was shown to a seat, turned to my right and recognised the woman sitting beside me, also waiting. Oh horror. I knew her, sort of. We'd had a few clashes banging our trolleys at the supermarket. I mean our trolleys met accidentally once, but oh the froideur that was unleashed. After that, a second instance in the aisle, Pia clicked her tongue when she saw me, and I swear she purposely bumped her trolley into mine. So then I did it to her the following time. I didn't know her name or anything. She was just that annoying person from the supermarket.

In the hormone specialist's waiting room we eyed each other warily. 'No trolley?' I asked. She laughed and asked me what I was doing there. She could probably guess, but instead of going into the gory details of why I was there (bleeding two weeks out of four for no discernible reason among other things), I said, 'Each night I wake up because my feet are shooting flaming darts at the wall. It keeps me up. When I finally fall asleep, my morning alarm is going off.'

'Just your feet?' She was intrigued. 'Not your whole body burning? Not your entire body being fed to the universe on the BBQ? Not your breasts in unbearable pain?'

This morning she sips her extra-shot large coffee and tells me that when a woman enters the menopause her shamanic qualities come to the fore. Shamanic qualities? I like the sound of this. I sneak a look at Alban, and he starts washing cups in the sink.

On this street, just two shops down from Alban's café is a new Colombian coffee house. Competition for him, he's not pleased. I haven't been there yet. I nudge Pia and lower my voice. 'We should go to the new place to learn to release our shamanic forces. They have quieter tables. Colombian coffee next week?'

'Why wait? Let's go now. We can do our research there.'

We breeze down to the new café. There are hessian sacks filled with coffee beans dotted about. Plants in the corners and on the tables. A different vibe. We order at the till. I ask for lemon-ginger tea, although I'm wondering if real dark hot chocolate is more shaman-like. Pia wants another extra-shot large coffee. We look around for an unobtrusive tucked-away table.

I'm hailed by Carla. She's sitting at a table with a friend. Carla is sometimes a guest teacher at the local yoga studio. She conducts the cocoa ceremony and yin yoga and sound baths, among other things. I feel her skills are unlimited. She's an uplifting person to be with because she has this habit of smiling widely and speaking in an upbeat tone. Everything is wonderful! How can she be so effervescent ALL THE TIME? I wonder if it ever gets annoying, or cloying, or untrue.

Not to me though, not in the small snatches of time that I see her. I always smile widely in her company and lose my reticence.

'How are you?' Carla asks.

She probably doesn't want to hear every detail of my life, but I stage whisper. 'Pia and I are going to release our shamanic selves. As a celebration of being post-menopausal. We are going to pour out the wisdom and kindness in our souls.'

'Reserve some for yourself,' Carla says. Then she speaks seriously. 'You know I'm a healer. I work with the body's chakras. I studied that. That's in your heritage. Why don't you follow that path?'

I'm puzzled. I don't know very much about shamans as yet. I know Carla's heritage is from South America. I remember her telling me she was Brazilian. Pia speaks out what I'm thinking: 'We don't want to learn chakra healing. We are creating rituals for menopause as we couldn't find any. We will strengthen and release our inner shamanic forces. Unless you say that it's reserved for people from a specific continent?'

'Oh, no no no,' Carla responds. 'My goodness. The same spirituality, the same powers, different words in different languages. Did you know Korean music is linked to shaman traditions?'

This is news to me. The world holds so much knowledge that I am clueless about. 'Everything is linked,' I say to Carla. 'Some of us feel that instinctively. But many people don't know and don't want to know.'

Carla nods amiably, eyes still sparkling. 'Shamans by different names, all over the world, not just South America. Aboriginal cultures, tribal people in the Indian subcontinent, Native North Americans, I could go on…' She makes a shooing motion with her nimble hands. 'Go on, part-shamans, have your coffee. Get your flow going.'

Peals of laughter, but we can't get mad at her, we have our ritual to perform.

Victoria Ekpo
A Summer Prematurely Here

I counted them
    All there
    Three days in a row
But it is February and although the crocuses came early,
With the light these days, warming the ground
That is not unusual
    But these?

The fingers of time
Promised a reprieve, some kind of hold
But here it is, as clammy as that monsoon afternoon
On a deserted Malaysian beach.

I'll wait for its eventual goodbye,
I'll do what they said I should do:
    Bid the days anew every time
     And dance to the songs of my grandmothers.
     Will their waters to flow, flow, flow
     Twirl, dance, swirl, flow,
     Will their waters flow.

Karen F Pierce
Nuclear Tingle (no one told me how my heart would feel)

I knew about the heat,
From nought to ninety-nine in seconds.
Had a medical pre-run in my thirties,
Trying to shrink the fibroids.
The globular tumours that betrayed my (as it turns out) barren womb,
And shed pints of blood and nauseating clots,
Left me glued to the bathroom for hours.
So yeah, I knew about the flushes, the flashes, the heat.
Well, I thought I did.
No one told me how my heart would feel.

Did I drink too much brandy and Babycham?
Lying heavy on the bed, wondering about the flutter and the tingle,
The heartache of vanished youth, or perhaps too many carbs?
Slow dawn of understanding,
It took a few explosions.
The almost indescribable, disconcerting, pins and needles, vellication within an organ,
That should not be tickled.
Breathe in, breathe out, stay calm, sip water,
You are not about to die,
Not yet.
It's just a forewarning.

Research reveals palpitations can be experienced.
Not quite the pulsating box I'd tick.
This warm quivering ominous creep,
Alerting me to the opening of furnace doors,
So I can brace myself for the nuclear blast of heat.
Incandescent soaking of bed sheets.
Middle-aged torrid blush, joked about *en masse.*
But I didn't anticipate my personal tingle,
And no one told me how my heart would feel.

Martha Patterson
Ruby-Red Jewel

A sweater worn, I'd take it off –
That cocoon of warmth, then chills,
And then repeating night sweats,
Like a dying flower, or a starfish
At the end of its life cycle,
And I seemed fated to expire

Still, I didn't miss the cramps
Though I missed Anne Frank's
Sweet secret she held dear,
Her solemn flag to femininity –
But honestly, regretful now?
No! I sparkle like a jewel!

JP Seabright
HUM PBA CK

I am a beached whale
   humpbacked   blubber-bound
   flailing   furiously   against the receding
tide   rounding out   my years
   grinding my bones   to dust
pulling my corsets   tight   my oestrogen
   trickling   through the   hourglass
I wear the patch   I am marked
   a cork-crumbled   dart board
   a slow-moving   bullseye
I declare a ceasefire   a drone-free zone
   a hormone replacement   bus service

Adele Evershed
Over the Bloody Moon

There is something called the double moon theory where people believe two spheres clashed together to make our moon. A bit like that Spice Girls' song when 2 become 1. And isn't menopause the opposite of this, when one body becomes two – a sci-fi movie, body snatcher invasion or some such.

I listen to Jeremy Vine on the radio. He is wearing a meno-vest, a garment designed to replicate the effect of hot flushes. Not a new idea. I remember Piers Morgan wearing a similar get-up to replicate labor and screaming. Always game for a laugh, he describes the vest and zips it up next to a mike so we all get to hear a noise like a fart. He feels a flush within a minute and describes the feeling as if he's on a beach and someone has taken away the parasol. And I think that's nothing like it.

The feeling of loss of control, your body doing something so out of the ordinary, no notice, is nothing like a day out at the seaside. But then he says, it's like his body has been taken over by someone else and there it is – my double body theory.

There is a waterfall of women who ring in and talk about their symptoms. The brain fog, the anxiety, the gamut of the forty-eight symptoms a woman might get, and Jeremy is polite when he cuts them off after a minute.

Then a man rings in. He had female hormones for prostrate cancer, suffers awful night sweats, and he talks for five whole minutes. It's awful and I feel for him but then I think isn't it typical a feature for women gets hijacked by a man. And I feel like howling at the moon.

My hot bod steps outside into the cool and makes like a she

wolf. And although my hubby looks up, he knows better than to comment. My other self walks back in and asks if he wants a cuppa? To my surprise he says, 'Sit down love. I'll make the tea.' And it's a small thing, and it's everything and I'm over the bloody moon.

Jane Burn
You have been this country I have known

I have gathered you on these small acres
                              these wads of pale land
You have pooled, ruddy, rusted iron   raw and deep, gusset slung
 I have mapped the islands that every night with you
                      left across my sheets   defiant skerries, ghosts
that no amount of soap could absolutely shift For thirty nine years
we have divided the night   you, vengeful and awaiting
every twist and turn my sleep has made   you, slithering free
         of each protective wing   your dried and dirty
mornings   your coastlines written into my clothes
We have crossed the distance between us month on month for what
seems forever You have travelled through my body, lost your hold
                      upon the walls of my womb
as I have travelled to you, marking out the calendar day and date
                  You are years of my life slipping away
The decades you came, clockwork prompt   every first day
         of term, shift, holiday   every party, date, exam
I have cursed your malevolence padded myself out, worn
         three pairs of knickers tights beneath trousers
                  sat on towels and still, you
                  soaked yourself into view
   It seems our love and hate affair is coming to a natural end
we visit less, like folk who only kept in touch for a while, for the sake
of politeness   The distance between us is measured
in occasional stains   I am cold, I am burning away
         This is a place I no longer know   where
are the old, familiar shapes   the trees, the ocean,

                    the monuments
I never wanted you   I think it is okay for me to say that now
I was never fond of the smell or the sight of blood   but
                thank you for the journey   I suppose
            Thank you wasted river for my child

Susan Cartwright-Smith
Dried

This happened without knowledge, without fanfare,
without blushing parcels handed,
voices lowered,
happened unremarkably,
no date in diary marked or anniversary kept,
but threshold crossed
and waymarkers still discovered
with the opening of
a seldom used handbag.
The beginning of this journey –
the other end –
is carved into my memory
the smell of hot coins
on my bloodied fingers.
Becoming woman
one day, changing all.
So what meaning is ascribed
the day when periods stop?
A cessation, an ending, the end.
Am I less a woman than
the day I was before?
I do not feel the change,
am still myself within.

Should I burn my Turin shrouds,
pants and sheets,
and take the scattering ashes
to a mountain top?
Like grieving relatives
carrying out a final wish.
Am I viewed as different, transitory,
in another phase?
I am now the crone –
so do I coil my hair into a bun,
keep counsel with the screech owl
and the secrets of the night?
Should I fold away my colours,
feel the stilling of my bones?
I shall not, for
the final period is not a dreaded date –
I will live each day
as if each day is new,
and find the purpose in the waning crescent,
continue to become.

Clare Starling
Evorel

This slim patch
is your way in
through my skin

a tab offered
on a tongue
should I take it?

hold my breath
my lusciousness
my diamond focus

I palm you
onto my thigh
rescue myself

a parched plain
watered. What will
surge through me now?

Ginger Strivelli
The Change

Space is cold. Except when you are going through the damn menopause! Zero gravity doesn't help hot flushes either. All in all, menopause is worse in outer space, Cassandra decided. Nonetheless she still complained when yet another hot flush hit her as she was trying to repair the docking clamps on the space station.

'Katie, turn the suit temp down. I'm roasting out here.'

'She's already set as low as she goes.'

'Why do they call things she…like ships…why are they always she?' Cassandra was straining with the huge wrench, it weighed nothing, literally, but it was still big and hard to work with in spacesuit gloves. 'Who started that? Had to be men. Only men worked on the old ships.'

'Look at us girls though,' Katie said. 'Out here in space, making history!'

'You aren't explaining to school kids now, Katie.'

'Ok, Grinch.'

'And as for 'girls'? I wish I was still a girl like you, honey, I'm an old woman, and I've got the white hair to prove it. Well, maybe not old, but a middle-aged woman going through menopause, at least, and let me tell you, you are not going to be look forward to this.'

Katie laughed. She knew all about Cassie and her sleeplessness or mood swings, she complained about them constantly, like Katie wouldn't have noticed. None of the crew were fond of Cassie's mood swings.

'Cass, you got company.' Katie's voice was suddenly serious.

'What?'

'Behind ya…what is that?'

Cassandra whirled around and let the wrench float as she came face to face with… Whatever it was, it was twice her size, not wearing a suit, glowing bright teal, and it had four… wings, maybe?

'You age, like me,' the creature said, somehow inside Cassandra's head. 'You no longer bleed as your birthers do.'

'What the actual…'

'Cass! First Contact Procedure!' Katie hollered in Cassandra's helmet, interrupting her. Cassandra pulled herself together.

'I am Cassandra. I am a human from Earth. We mean no harm to any being living in space or on other worlds. We are peaceful explorers,' she repeated the memorised greeting.

'You age. You are mature and wise, like me,' the alien said and swept closer to Cassandra, giving her some sort of four-winged hug.

Cassandra's hot flush passed as her blood ran cold at the being's touch. It had somehow touched her skin to skin, through her spacesuit, just as it somehow spoke to her, mind to mind.

'Cass? You okay? I've alerted mission control. General Markus said we are imagining it, and not to mention it on the open channel.'

'Hysterical. I bet you he will claim we are both just hysterical.'

The being had fluttered her wings, taking herself a metre back from Cassandra. Cassandra tried to show a non-threatening smile to the creature. It didn't really have the equipment to smile, but Cassandra thought that the three eyes looked friendly-ish.

'We came to welcome you into your wisdom. We have watched your tribe dabbling here in the abyss. You are such

76

cute creatures. We did not know your kind came into the wisdom though, as none before you have done so out here.'

'Into the wisdom, Menopause? No, mostly men out here before me, and a few younger women. They have just started to let a more diverse crowd into the astronaut programme. My best friend is the first disabled astronaut. She's autistic. I'm the first older woman, I guess.'

'How strange your kind waited to send the most qualified out here to explore.' The being's skin changed colour from teal to periwinkle to magenta.

'We are a strange race,' Cassandra agreed. 'Katie, you got anywhere with mission control?'

'Nope. They say we are hallucinating, and they want me to run diagnostics on the life support… and want us both examined by the doctors.'

'Hallucinations? Huh!' Cassandra turned back to the alien. 'I'm the first woman going through the change that you have observed?'

'The change. What a poetic and accurate way of describing coming into your wisdom. I will tell my people that beautiful phrase. I send my sympathy to your young friend Katie that she is yet too young to join us in the change. I wish her luck in doing so in the future.'

'Yeah, um, okay, thanks.' Katie didn't like the being talking inside her head any more than Cassandra did.

The alien began backing away, flying or swimming or walking; Cassandra could not really put words to how the being moved. Out of habit, and in shock, she held up a hand to wave as it departed. Oddly, it waved back with one of its wings.

Katie was arguing on the top-secret channel with mission control that they had indeed just made first contact with aliens. The general, as Cassandra predicted, used the word 'hysterical', which made Katie lose her composure and she told him and his horse where to go and what to do with themselves.

Cassandra pushed a couple of buttons on the cuff of her space suit.

Instantly, on the public channel that every news station and elementary school on Earth could see, the live feed of the glowing winged alien moving away from Cassandra was broadcast in real time. Cassandra waved at her again so the alien would wave back. The gasps from around the world could just about be heard up in space.

'Now you are hysterical too, General, along with the rest of Mother Earth's children, 'cause right there, Sir, is the alien I just spoke to.' Cassandra laughed as another hot flush hit her.

Anne Caldwell
China

Time is pickled in this empty nest. You loathe the phrase, but your heart flutters against ribs, like a decoy crow in a Larsen trap on the moors. You're caged in a Sunday house, fridge humming to itself. August rains blur the purple bloom of ling and bell heather. Days are swollen and sore. Your child has spread her wings, a coach ticket to Venice and Spotify streaming happiness along the autobahns. You work all day then wander through the curtained rooms; pick up damp towels, stack laundered linen, sense the fury of unused china on the Welsh dresser.

Anne Eccleshall
natural wastage

at work everyone else grew
taller louder defter
my voice wore out   i left

now my skin no longer fits
it hangs off the back of my arms
folds under my chin

colour has leeched from my hair
i fade in and out, freeze
muted without warning

today i stood in the road
to let parents, school kids pass
not one of them noticed

me shrinking in the gutter
heard me say thank you
perhaps it was in my head

the doctor calls it atrophy
says its normal to lose bones
i should drink more water

Chloe Balcomb
Gutsy Menopausal Woman

I'm a menopausal woman,
ride waves of heat, can't sleep for days,
my memory shot, my thoughts ablaze,
my nipples pale, my breasts slung low,
my bladder weak, reactions slow.
Strange rashes bloom across my chest,
I can't stand noise; I need more rest.
No longer sharp or young or slim,
I'm scarred by loss, my eyes grown dim.
And see these feet no longer fleet?
They've flattened out, complain and creak.
But to hell with all the gripes and fears,
I've gained new riches with the years –
I'm done with guilt, the need to serve,
I claim my place, my joy and verve,
I have a love that's sweet and slow,
that thrills my skin from head to toe,
I speak my truth, have time to write,
need no endorsement, travel light.
No going back, I've broken free,
now who I am is what you see –
a gutsy menopausal woman.

Mary Mulholland
O Womb

Ours was never an easy relationship.
Forgive me for not caring for you more.
Your arrival caught me unaware.
No one warned me you'd be coming,
or that I'd start to count the days until
your next erratic visit. You blamed me,
said I'd become too thin. I wasn't
bothered. Who wants a curse? Doctors
forced us into a truce. You responded
with swathes of blood, filled buckets.
To combat this, I grew rosy fat, grew
babies. At last, you were content and I
told myself, o womb, I should be too:
isn't this what women are supposed to do?

Suddenly, as you came, one day you left.
Along with my children, grown, and husband,
already gone. For the first time on my own,
fully alone, I drifted lost till someone asked
who I was. I didn't speak to strangers but
that wasn't my reason I couldn't reply.

My therapist told me to try writing labels:
daughter, mother, I could be a grandmother
soon. Is life only to perpetuate our kind,
or is it too late to aim for more? Walking
home in the dark, I pause and a street lamp
encircles me in light: why not trek real deserts,
climb physical mountains, access my power.
You see, o womb, you can't stop me anymore.

Amanda Addison
Silver Swans

It starts with our feet. They stand firmly on the ground before we bend our toes to *demi-pointe* and on to full *pointe*. '*Jeté*,' she calls over and over. *Jeté* is from the French and means to throw. Obediently we cast out our legs, transferring the weight from one foot to the other. Our supporting legs set into concrete pillars around the village hall. We suspend our legs in mid-air as if they're weightless, and point our toes.

The teacher says toes, I hear the word toys. A slip in pronunciation from Ukrainian to English, almost, but not quite the right sound. We are a long way from Odessa. But then we are dancing to Tchaikovsky's *Nutcracker* suite, and it is all about the toys as we race forward towards Christmas.

At the ballet barre, supported yet unsupported, we hold a *grand plié* as tight as an elastic band about to snap. Each week we bend a little further, stand a little taller. We are fully present, in the moment, otherwise one wrong movement: a straight elbow, an unengaged core, shoulder wings up instead of down – and we've lost it. Stay present. Stay with the music and we can ascend beyond what we thought possible. We are weightless. We are flying. A bird's-eye view of possibilities, a renewed strength and elegance we never thought possible. We have changed and are transformed. We are growing taller, 'another inch by summer,' says our teacher. Better that than shrinking and retiring into oblivion.

The music is no longer an external rhythm, no longer a noise playing out through a phone connected to a portable speaker in the corner. The days of my childhood are long gone, days when a pianist sat at the corner and played along. We are mostly in our fifties, one us is over sixty, becoming silver swans and taking on a new challenge. Nevertheless, the music has seeped through our feet bundled into tight pink and black shoes, through tights, through our skin to become our own beating heart, striking right to our fully engaged core. We are transported to another world. Breathless and breath-taking across the floor, our stage to the world, we move beyond our comfort zone.

We cool down. Through the window the sky turns to flaming orange and it is only four in the afternoon. A flat land of big skies. A county of air bases and flight paths. A rumble and then louder and louder a drone of a gigantic grey whale of an aircraft soars noisily overhead. And in this moment of distraction the gentle *Waltz of the Flowers* is drowned out. Our teacher speaks to us intimately. She speaks of breakfast with her host family. 'When one of those planes first flew over I wept. My daughter hid under the table.'

We pause. We hold our breath. The air is charged. 'Then my hosts told me they are training Ukrainian pilots.' She smiles. 'So now when they fly over we look up and wave.'

Срібні лебеді
Аманда Еддісон

Це починається з наших ніг. Вони міцно стоять на землі до того, як ми поступово підгинаємо пальці і далі повністю встаємо навшпиньки. «Jeté», — знову й знову вигукує вона. Jeté походить з французької і означає «кидати». Слухняно викидаємо ноги, переносячи вагу з однієї ноги на іншу. Наші балетні станки прикріплені до бетонних колон у залі сільського клубу. Ми утримуємо ноги в повітрі, ніби вони невагомі, і тягнемо пальці.

Учителька каже «toes» — «пальці ніг», а я чую слово «toys» — «іграшки». Це незначна помилка в англійській вимові українки, схоже, але не зовсім правильне звучання слова. Ми дуже далеко від Одеси. Але все ж танцюємо під сюїту з Лускунчика Чайковського, і це все про іграшки, поки ми мчимо вперед до Різдва.

Біля балетної жердини, з підтримкою і без, ми тримаємо гранд-пліє з напругою еластичної стрічки, яка наче ось-ось лусне. Щотижня ми присідаємо трохи нижче, встаємо трохи вище. Ми повністю присутні в цьому моменті, адже один неправильний рух — прямий лікоть, незадіяна спина, лопатки підняті, а не опущені, — і ми його втратимо. Ми тут і зараз. Ми з музикою і тому можемо піднятися за межі доступного. Ми невагомі. Ми летимо. Дивимося з висоти пташиного польоту на можливості, відновлену силу й елегантність, про які ніколи не думали, що вони досяжні. Ми змінюємося і трансформуємося. Виростаємо. «Ще один дюйм до літа», — каже наша вчителька. Краще це, ніж зміліти і піти в забуття.

Музика більше не є зовнішнім ритмом, більше не є шумом, що лунає з телефона, підключеного до портативної колонки. Давно минули часи мого дитинства, коли піаніст сидів у кутку й акомпанував. Нам здебільшого за п'ятдесят, одному за шістдесят, ми стаємо срібними лебедями та приймаємо новий виклик. Попри все, музика просочується крізь наші ноги, закуті в тісні рожеві та чорні туфлі, крізь колготки, крізь нашу шкіру, щоб стати нашим власним серцем, яке б'ється, вражаючи прямо в наше повністю задіяне нутро. Ми переносимося в інший світ. Задихаючись і затримуючи дихання на підлозі, нашій сцені, ми перетинаємо межі зони комфорту.

Ми поволі заспокоюємося. За вікном небо стає полум'яно-помаранчевим, а це ж лише четверта по обіді. Рівнинна земля великих небес. Графство авіабаз і шляхів польоту. Над головою лунає гуркіт, а потім усе голосніше й голосніше — гул гігантського сірого киталітака. І цю мить, поки ми відволікаємось, заглушає ніжний Вальс Квітів. Наша вчителька розмовляє з нами душевно. Вона розповідає про сніданок з родиною, у якої гостює. «Коли один із цих літаків пролетів уперше, я заплакала. Моя дочка схвилалася під столом».

Ми завмираємо. Затримуємо подих. Напруга в повітрі. «Тоді господарі мені сказали, що це тренуються українські пілоти, — вона посміхається. — Тож тепер, коли вони пролітають, ми дивимося вгору й махаємо рукою».

Tessa Lang
Monthly

I wait on the flat roof
at the top of my house,
a shivering midwife
willing a skinny new moon
to emerge, footling and pallid,
through a slit in murky cloud.
Every month I attend her,
bearing the tattered gifts
and hopeless promises of
the next fresh start.
Nothing yet. I wait as
red lights deck cranes and
high-rise windows glow
brighter than her stillborn spark,
a star in a teacup, a memory of light.

Victoria Bailey
Men – oh – paused

My periods went away and in my most radical move ever, I paused men. I refused to immerse myself in their words, take their art to heart, listen to their proclamations, seek out their opinions, pay for their services, search for their songs, care what they thought, follow their gaze, because there aren't always two sides to every story. And now I make space in my life only for women, because so much of what they have to share is still so often overlooked, and once they're gone, they're gone.

> I want to be born
> again and rebuilt without
> the input of men.

Elizabeth A Richter
Demeter

Back when I talked to Dr. Jones about getting rid of the thing
He said – trying, but completely failing,
to respond adequately to the grief I felt at my impending loss –
'Sometimes we aren't intended to leave this world
with the same number of pots and pans we started with.'

He was talking, not about kitchenware, but about my uterus
sinking down like a heavy football into my vagina.
It keeps me sitting on the toilet waiting for my bladder to empty,
resting on the stretched bow of my ureter,
too heavy to be shot back into place.
And the golden urine, backed up well beyond its time,
turns cloudy, teaming with bacteria.
Then I think I'm done, but ten minutes later,
I'm back again – same pain, same pressure.
Sometimes I don't even want to leave the house or even the bedroom.

My womb is the place of life, all life, my life.
It is a hidden place, from which all things grow.
It is my home where I have my china set safely stored
in the cabinet, waiting for holidays and other special occasions.
The diplomas on the walls, my jewellery case filled to the brim
with a lifetime of collection, my own as well as my mother's.
It is the mats to protect the tables, the tablecloths,
my pantry stocked and the refrigerator humming and bulging
with food.

It is all my riches and my stores,
my fireside, my community, my nation, humanity itself.
When it convulses in bed with you, this is because I love you
and it will bring back the summer and the corn will grow.

I fear if I let it go, if I lose it
I will lose the complex depths of my mind and imagination,
the rich, flowing River Nile and the Euphrates River Valley,
these pounding fingers typing figures onto the page
that make me sing with the universe.
What am I without this patiently hibernating vessel
from which my children emerged, wet, protesting, blind, alien?

If I lose it, will I become an unnatured, empty pot
or is this fear a mere superstition, a deluded synchronicity,
a phantasm from the ancient well?

Ruth Higgins
Her Mid-life Performance Review

has been going well and things are as usual
                              until she sits down and misses the chair
a forgotten cup of tea spills over her shoes
                                        a wrecking ball destroys her desk
knocks her through the window opposite
                                        she lands painfully in the car park
a tree rocked by high winds falls on her causing carnage

        damning evidence metamorphoses in the women's loo
prompting Candice (Head of HR) to send round an email
                    asking the lady who has committed this foul act
to return to the cubicle in question and

                    Do the Right Thing

                              She strips off blood-stained underwear
runs through the office block
                                        all floors screaming
traffic outside cranes its neck
                    to make out *fuck you* in blood backwards
on one cracked pane up there.

Jane McLaughlin
The Farmer's Fire

The temperature is minus three and I am burning. It is six o' clock on a January morning. I look out of the kitchen window and the frost is thick on the fields.

The early morning farmer, as people think. He gets up at 5.30 and in winter puts on a balaclava and warm clothes and stumps out to sort the milking in the dark.

He isn't a woman. He isn't a woman in the menopause.

I step outside into the yard. I haven't put a coat on. Just a t-shirt and jeans, and gloves, because the fire does not always go down to the fingers. It's been happening for two years now. It could go on for ten. And the dizziness, the shaking, the brain fog. It is not possible.

The sky is clear and a paleness begins to show in the east.

The sound of a car coming up the track to the yard. Headlights. Haydon the cowman parks up by the winter shed. Big coat, big boots.

He and I work, only speaking when we need to. But he watches me, with the machines, with the chemicals. He knows about the fire and the fog.

There are already two calves that we need to care for, to make sure they are feeding, that they are warm and dry. There are pregnant cows that we need to check to see if they could be going into labour and to give them feed and minerals.

Apart from that it is the milking machines, checking the feed and water, checking the beds in the cubicles.

The face first. Flaming and itching. Then the neck, shoulders, chest. As if the blood boils. Sweat pours. I stop work on the milking machines and stand still, hoping the dizziness will pass. Haydon looks at me, says nothing.

Flush. Flash the Americans call it, which seems closer to the truth. What is flush? Water going down a toilet, a bloom of flowers, five cards of the same suit. Flash is lightning, a signal from a lighthouse, a moment.

The lights in the shed are warm, the air moist with animal breath, the heavy cowshed smell weights the air.

Two cows may have mastitis and need to be separated. Another shows early signs of labour. A big Holstein like the rest, prolific milkers, the electric light reflecting on her black and white coat.

So many births, so many milkings, and none of them mine.

These days they tell me milk is abuse. That the calves are murdered. I can't cope with that. It is how I live, the only way I know, and hard enough to live from it at all these days. My cows are healthy and for as long as they live are well-kept and comfortable. I don't love them individually but I love their big warm presence, the sight of them out in the fields in summer, even their fleshy earthy smell.

If I'd had children they would have enjoyed rearing the calves. The males go to beef breeders. Farming is a business and I have to accept that some people don't like it.

Most animals do not have menopause. Only us and the whales. Pilot whales, belugas, orcas, narwhals. Ceasing to reproduce is an anomaly. Except where you cannot.

Cold water mammals. That long twisted horn of the narwhal. I had a story book once about a narwhal that wanted a hat for its birthday.

Do whales burn as their fertility shuts down?

Subsiding a little. I start work on the machines again, fixing the teat cups, starting the pumps. I think of the cold water at the bottom of the hill. That little lake with its reedy island where swans nest. Out there in the icy darkness. Such cold, cold water.

Rest, they say. Try to relax, talk to your employer to see how they can help.

My farm. My father's farm. Then my mother's. The only place I have ever wanted to be, the only thing I have ever wanted to do. And now the struggle to hold it, to keep it from sliding into ruinous debt. In summer the best place anyone could wish to be, a honey-coloured stone house on a flowery hill. In winter the unceasing battle with mud, rain, disease.

Cold water, warm water. Hypothermia. What is the opposite? Must be a word for it.

What happens: the body temperature drops. Shivering. Mental confusion. Then hallucinations. After that you slide into a sense of warmth, of comfort and well-being, as everything starts to shut down.

Sleep. The early mornings do not matter because sometimes sleep does not happen at all now. Sometimes not even getting into bed but just pulling a chair up to the range and listening to whatever comes in on the airwaves.

The two calves are doing fine, feeding well.

I saw that harp seals have milk for twelve days. Then they are exhausted and leave the baby to survive, or not, on the ice. People cried and flooded social media with their grief.

It is getting light outside but the sun is not yet up.

The heat in my body is too much now, I have to leave the shed.

I go out and walk through the yard. The cold hits me: the burning does not stop but my head clears. A body like a walking forest fire, a mind that curdles like week-old milk.

The water.

Down the track between the frosty fields.

Through the gate to the lower meadow. Across the crackle of frozen grass. Light growing in the east, beginning to shine on the water. Perhaps a thin skim of ice at the edge, under the reeds.

I take off my clothes and drop them on the ground. I step into the water. My feet sink into the cold mud and at last the shock of the water numbs my fire. I slide in. So cold, so calm, so peaceful.

To let go. Of milking, of calves, of dark bitter mornings.

Warm. Comfortable. Drifting.

I sense the day is brighter but I have no sense of time.

The sun has come up and is shining in my eyes.

A yellow winter sun, making a brilliant path across the water.

I can hear something. Is it a bird, or the sound of a calf calling for its mother?

Today there will be another calf and as the month goes on there will be more.

A fire cannot burn forever.

I have to get the day's milk away.

I start to swim into the sun's path. My arms are sluggish, clogged by the strangeness of the freezing water, I can hardly get my legs to move, but as I try, they start to loosen. I kick more strongly, my arms beat with something like the strength of summer. The water is bright around me.

I swim into the morning.

Em Gray
Wilding

That old red suit, those devilled eggs –
four hundred and thirty-seven funerals
for a grief not mine.

Now from your broken furious battery hen
this wringing of plagues

and I terrariummed
with night rains, impregnable
fog, that moon face
like a questioning Aunt's,
eclipsed.

But too, this rage of wildfires
razing to swidden – see
horizon's spread,

what buds.

Claire Booker
On Discovering a New Energy Source

Forget fracking, turbines, that old slow coal –
my kick-ass cells have begun firing on testosterone,
love the no-nonsense punch of it. Just watch
them blaze tracks. I'm a one-woman energy surge,
a furnace that devours cant. Try me with those looks –
you'll yelp, foot to foot, on my desert sands.
When I plunge into the sea, it hisses with body heat.
I can't be bent, buckled, blundered, back-pedalled,
pistoned off. I'm a fugue in the key of M, a hot-air
balloon rising on its own vapour. Who needs sandbags?
I float above rain forests, Antarctica, the flooded
levees of my many mistakes, head for the moon,
turn it Bloody Mary red. My warmth's no longer feathery.
These feet scorch rock, turn history to ash. I'm a sweat
lodge, a holy thing. I part waves, create weather patterns,
sit in my underwear for the breeze, because I dare,
because I'm stoked and ready.

Enough Already
Claire Lynn

I say to you both: your work here is done.
Retire. Sell up. Settle on the south coast
and there recline in deckchairs in the sun.

Forty years you have toiled, month after month
– regular, stalwart, persistent – and so
I say to you both, your work now is done.

Sit down, watch the waves, and let the tide run
to the moon's pull, which will leave you alone
once you retire to deckchairs in the sun.

Never again, not this month, not next one.
You have nothing to prove, no more to show.
I say to you now: Your work here is done;

there's no need to use up the very last one.
Leave them be, let them addle, learn to say No.
Doze and decline in deckchairs in the sun.

Enough already. This is fruitless. Shun
the swelling, the shedding, the cycle, the flow.
I say to you both, your work here is done.
Let go. Recline in deckchairs in the sun.

About Arachne Press

Arachne Press is a micro publisher of (award-winning!) short story and poetry anthologies and collections, novels including a Carnegie Medal nominated young adult novel, and a photographic portrait collection.

We are expanding our range all the time, but the short form is our first love. We keep fiction and poetry live, through readings, festivals (in particular our Solstice Shorts Festival), workshops, exhibitions and all things to do with writing.

https://arachnepress.com/

Follow us on Twitter:
@ArachnePress
@SolShorts

and Instagram
@ArachnePress

Like us on Facebook:
@ArachnePress
@SolsticeShorts2014

Find out more about our authors at
https://arachnepress.com/writers/

Printed in the USA
CPSIA information can be obtained
at www.ICGtesting.com
LVHW071242091123
763482LV00032B/554